'Home, Olaf, and don't spare the Norses.'

Summer with Monika
After the Merrymaking
Gig
In the Glassroom
Holiday on Death Row
Waving at Trains
Melting into the Foreground
Blazing Fruit (Selected Poems, Volume One)
You at the Back (Selected Poems, Volume Two)
Defying Gravity

Roger McGough

Sporting Relations

With illustrations by the author

VIKING

VIKING

Published by the Penguin Group
Penguin Books Ltd, 27 Wrights Lane, London w8 5tz, England
Penguin Books USA Inc., 375 Hudson Street, New York, New York 10014, USA
Penguin Books Australia Ltd, Ringwood, Victoria, Australia
Penguin Books Canada Ltd, 10 Alcorn Avenue, Toronto, Ontario, Canada m4v 3b2
Penguin Books (NZ) Ltd, 182–190 Wairau Road, Auckland 10, New Zealand

Penguin Books Ltd, Registered Offices: Harmondsworth, Middlesex, England

First published by Methuen 1974
This expanded and revised edition published by Viking 1996
10 9 8 7 6 5 4 3 2 1

Set in 11/14pt Monotype Baskerville
Designed in QuarkXpress on an Apple Macintosh
Printed in Great Britain by Butler & Tanner Ltd, Frome and London

A CIP catalogue record for this book is available from the British Library

isbn 0–670–86883–3

Contents

Grandma 1
Uncle Fergie 2
Uncle Malcolm 3
Cousin Wystan 4
Uncle Mork 6
Uncle Pat 7
Big Ed and Little Ed 8
Cousin Caroline 9
Uncle Anthony 10
Jennifer Chubb-Challoner 11
Kung Fu Lee 11
Albert Robinson 12
Cousin Chas 14
Aunty Dora 16
Aunt Ermintrude 18
Cousin Eva 19
Susie and Nell 20
Uncle Bram 22
Billy Our Kid 23
Wild Bill Sitting Bull 24
Uncle Mo 25
Uncle Noah 26
Granny 28

Dear Lonely Hearts   28
Cousin Reggie   29
Onkle Fritz   30
Kirsten   30
Frau Brünnhilde   31
Angelina   32
Uncle Philip   33
Uncle Sean   34
Merve the Swerve   35
Terry and Pancho   36
Uncle Jack   37
Uncle Trevor and Aunty Penny   38
Cousin Horatio   39
Alf   40
Alfreda   41
Cousin Fosbury   42
Cousin Ivor   43
Aunt Agatha   44
Uncle 'enery   46
Old Mac   47
Eno   48
Marvin   49
Uncle Terry   50

Barry Bungee   52
Uncle Jason   54
Cousin Christ   55
Cousin Fiona   56
Maybelline   58
Big Arth   60
Accrington Stan   62
The Hon. Nicholas Frayn   63
Aunty Ann   64
Uncle Leo   66
Uncle Len   67
Elmer Hoover   68
Uncle Jed   69
Cousin Daisy   70
Cousin Nell   71

Grandma

Grandma
(All-England Cartwheeling
Champion 1944–49)
thought romance was dead

Fig. 1

Until she met Grandpa
(a somersaulter of note)
at a Rotary Club dance
and fell heels over head.

Once wed
they backflipped
down the aisle
in breathtaking style

Then cartwheeled like clockwork
throughout the day
to spend their honeymoon
unwinding, in Morecambe Bay.

Fig. 2

1

Fig 3

Uncle Fergie

Uncle Fergie
was a famed caber tosser.

As a caber tosser
he had no peer.

It is rumoured
he could toss a caber
from there

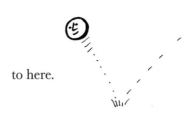

to here.

Uncle Malcolm

Uncle Malcolm
put the shot
for Scotland.

When he retired
he collected shots
as a hobby.

At the time
of his death
he had nearly 200.

And in accordance
with his last wishes
they were buried with him

at St Giles Cemetery in Perth.
Uncle Mal is now at rest
somewhere near the centre of the earth.

Cousin Wystan

Train-spotting
is that a sport?

It is for Cousin Wystan
until he gets caught

Armed with a paint-box
and a quiver of brushes

Around the railsheds
after midnight he rushes

He's the Seurat of the Circle Line
the Northern's Jackson Pollock

His trainscapes are spectacular
surreal, yet melancholic

His dabs and daubs deservedly
stir the imagination

Critics applaud each masterpiece
as it rattles through the station

4

The National and the Tate
compete for his first retro

And Paris implores him
to immortalize the Metro

But Wystan is unmoved
by popular acclaim

And dreams, not of money,
galleries or fame

But of airports,
Heathrow, Schiphol, JFK.

Security Alert!
Wystan (plane-spotter) is on his way.

Uncle Mork

Uncle Mork
was a fell-walker.
He'd take off from York
and walk and walk

over the dales
across the moors
through the vales
blisters, sores

it hurt like hell.
He walked and walked
and never talked
just walked and walked

until he fell.

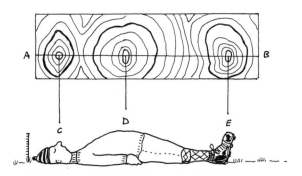

Uncle Pat

Going into bat
against the Windies
in his first (and final) Test
Uncle Pat
wore vinyl undies
and an armour-plated vest.

But in the panic to get dressed
(wickets falling thick and fast)
left his box off.

Third ball took his rocks off.

Big Ed and Little Ed

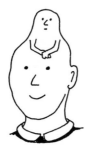

Big Ed and Little Ed
are a referee
Two Eds are better than one
don't you agree?

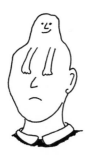

Cousin Caroline

Cousin Caroline
was a very fine
sprinter. In the winter
of 1988, with a
bandaged knee
she ran the 100
metres in 10.3

But her best time
was in the dressing room afterwards.

Uncle Anthony

Uncle Anthony
was a low hurdler.
Being only 4′ 6″
he was the lowest
hurdler in Bridlington.

In his summer of '42
he married a Northern Counties
high jumper, who,
delighted to please,
being 2 foot taller,
straddled him with ease.

Jennifer Chubb-Challoner

Jennifer Chubb-Challoner
the Cheltenham Ladies
Triple Jump Champion

was first spotted
by a peepingtom talentscout
while still at Junior School

when she won
the 3-legged race
all on her own.

Kung Fu Lee

Kung Fu Lee
a greenbelt
with a reputation second to none
was more than vexed
when annexed
and one morning built upon.

Albert Robinson

Albert Robinson
(a half-cousin by marriage)
is probably the only
bullfighter in Birmingham.

At five in the afternoon
he parades round the Bull Ring
in his Suit of Lights
(an army battledress
and panty tights
sequinned plimsolls
and padded flies)
a faraway look
in his faraway eyes.

For he struts beneath
Andalusian skies
as concrete corridors
echo the cries
of aficionados
in shoppers' disguise:
'El Robbo, El Robbo, el mas valiente matador!'

On his way to the hostel
he stops and he buys
a carton of milk
and two meat pies
then it's olé to bed
and olé to rise.

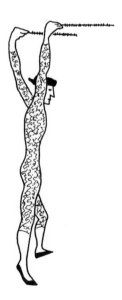

Cousin Chas

Cousin Chas,
an expert in the art
of self-defence,
would go out of his way
to defend himself.

'In an age
of senseless violence,'
he would hiss,
'there is only one language
people understand
and it's this.'

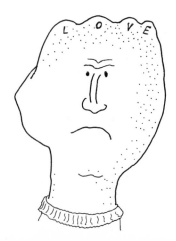

Every Saturdaynight
after a few pints
Chas and his mates
would roam the streets
looking for pale young men
against whom
they would defend themselves.

Cousin Chas
may not have been
one of Nature's gentlemen
but he was a right bastard.

Aunty Dora

A grandpiano of a woman is Aunty Dora.
Limbering up on the 60-metre board
she throws the pool into shadow.

What with the shaking and the creaking
a spectator might expect a soaking
a depthcharge of nuclear proportions

> But no.
> Her dive
> is as
> delicate
> as an
> hibiscus
> unfolding
> in slowmo.

Like thistledown on the air
she drifts, turns, almost lingers there
until her fingers tap the meniscus

The surface opens soundlessly
and pulling in her shadow after her
Aunty Dora and water are one.

Aunt Ermintrude

Aunt Ermintrude
was determined to
swim across the Channel.
Each week she'd
practise in the bath
encostumèd in flannel.

The tap end
was Cap Gris Nez
the slippy slopes
were Dover. She'd
doggypaddle up and down
vaselined all over.

After 18 months, Aunt Erm was in peak condition.
So, one cold grey morning in March
she boarded the Channel steamer at Dover
went straight to her cabin
climbed into the bath
and urged on by a few well-wishers,
Aunt Ermintrude, completely nude
swam all the way to France.
Vive la tante!

BRAVO
BRAVO

Cousin Eva

Cousin Eva
a deep-sea diva
never sang at the Met.

Not only too wet
but too snotty

which drove
Pavarotti
potty.

Susie and Nell

Synchronized swimmers
    were Susie and Nell
synchronized walkers
    and talkers as well.

At their first Olympics
They swept the board.

Synchronized sweepers
    were Nelly and Sue
Synchronized sleepers
    and sleepwalkers too.

At their second Olympics
The Board swept them.

It all went sour
    one day in the shower
when Nell slipped
    and fell on the floor
her head flew off
    and rolled under the door.

Next morning
It was splashed over the tabloids:
OLYMPIC CHAMPS (*dash*) ANDROIDS!

Uncle Bram

Uncle Bram
a batcatcher of distinction
scorned the use of
battraps, batnets and batpoison.
'Newfangled nonsense,'
he would scoff, and off
he would go
to hang upsidedown
in belfries
for days on end
in the hope of snatching
one of the little batstards.

Billy Our Kid

Billy our Kid
was the dandy
of the snooker halls
He affected
brocade waistcoats
of uncertain hue
and with his trusty
pearlhandled cue
hustled many an
amateur passerthrough.

In '69 he went to New Orleans
to try his luck.
Now he lives in Pittsburgh
and drives a truck.

Wild Bill Sitting Bull

Wild Bill Sitting Bull
(half cowboy, half Sioux)
confused by watching Westerns
went in search of caribou.

In the Badlands
he was strangled
by his spangled lassoo

Did a wardance
then scalped himself
like a man's gotta do.

Uncle Mo

Uncle Mo
a shy bachelor of 43
was a nudist at heart.

Suddenly last summer
he formed a club
for bashful sunworshippers

who met in his greenhouse
every weekend
dressed to the nines.

Quiet as tomatoes
they thought allsorts,
sweating profanely.

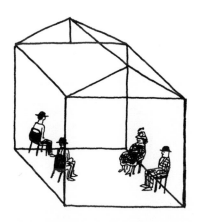

Uncle Noah

A man mountain
   was Uncle Noah
the best hammer-thrower
   in Western Samoa.

Once, in the midst
   of a magnificent throw
he lost concentration
   and forgot to let go.

Flew out of the stadium
   and up into space
a puzzled expression
   on his pustular face.

At first it was fun
   in a stomach-churning way
but once round the planet
   he called it a day.

Free of encumbrance
  the ex-hammer-thrower
plummeted earthwards
  towards Krakatoa.

Into the mouth
  of the crater he rushed
right down its throat
  like a finger, pushed.

With a gulp disappeared
  into the bubbling lava
the volcano heaved
  and threw up over Java.

Since the eruption, experts say,
  of mighty Krakatoa
Sunsets have been spectacular
  (so, thank you, Uncle Noah).

Granny

Granny plays whist
better when pwhist.

Dear Lonely Hearts

'Dear Lonely Hearts,
my name is Nate
my hobbies are weightlifting
and tempting fate.'

'Dear Nate,
my name is Kate
my hobby is weightwatching
please name the date.'

He showered her with gifts
Now Kate watches as Nate lifts.

Cousin Reggie

Cousin Reggie
who adores the sea
lives in the Midlands
unfortunately.

He surfs down escalators
in department stores
and swims in the High Street
on all of his fours.

Sunbathes on the pavement
paddles in the gutter
(I think our Reggie's
a bit of a nutter).

Onkle Fritz

'In shorts and vest a Cresta run
without a sleigh is fun.'

So claimed Onkle Fritz
now enAlped in little bits.

Kirsten

Kirsten was first on the nursery slopes

Did she like it? She did not

Swerved to avoid a rocking-horse

And crashed into a cot.

Frau Brünnhilde

Frau Brünnhilde
wrestled in mud.
At wrestling in mud
she was terribly good.

She wore tight
Lederhosen
and each night
sprayed a hose on
the front three rows.
How they booed!

After each rude bout
men queued outside
and vied to take her home.
Lick off the caked mud
and drink Liebfraumilch
from her silk
jackboots.

Angelina

Angelina
(blueblooded)
owned a yacht
and smoked pacht
a lacht.
So when things
gacht hacht
away sailed Angelina
(so regal)
to where the grass was greener
(and legal).

BLACHT →

Uncle Philip

Uncle Philip was hopeless at waterpolo
it just wasn't the game for him
for starters he was colourblind
and besides he couldn't swim.

Banned from English swimming pools
for disobeying basic rules
he emigrated to Eire
where officials were fairer.

From Donegal to Bantry Bay
audiences he astounded
until one fateful Galway day
when his polopony drownded.

Uncle Sean

If they held Olympic contests
for brick-throwing
Uncle Sean would win them all
at all.

But they don't.
So he carries hods for Wimpeys
and dreams of glories
that might have been.

Uncle Sean lives in Coventry
a stone's throw away
from the Albert Hall
at all.

Merve the Swerve

Merve the Swerve
 an old tennis pro

Won the French Open
 the US and oh!

He started snorting
 lines of snow

Umpires warned
 it would end in tears

Now Mervyn's serving
 seven years.

Terry and Pancho

Last year
Terry and Pancho
won the Men's Doubles.

One had ... uhm ... troubles.
They were fixed.

This year
Terri and Pancho
won the Mixed.

Uncle Jack

Uncle Jack
was a very cross
country runner.
Nothing seemed
to make him happy.

With only one lung
he couldn't run fast
so he took short cuts
and still came last.

And meaner still
of Uncle Jack
some of the short cuts he took
he never gave back.

Uncle Trevor and Aunty Penny

Uncle Trevor and Aunty Penny
won the Northamptonshire
ballroom dancing championship
seven times on the foxtrot.

Practice makes perfect.
Every night after saying their prayers
they glide round the bedroom
for hours on end.

(The nightdress Aunty Penny
wears, she made herself
out of 250 yards
of floral winceyette.)

Uncle Trevor, however,
made of sterner stuff
to's and fro'ze
in the buff.

Cousin Horatio

Cousin Horatio
won a ten pound bet
by rowing across the Atlantic
singlehanded. Six months later
he confessed to having used
both hands, and rather
than face public scorn
sailed from Exmouth
one grey dawn
wrote up his log
tidily
then committed himself to the deep
suicidily.

Alf

Alf
on his day off from Billy Smart's,
tarts himself up. Puts on
his best monkey boots and braces
and races down to Clacton with his mates.
He hates so much it features
as a gruesome tattoo.
Pea-brained and circus-trained
a skinhead through and through.

Alf
is famous for his fighting skills
and rightly so.
He knocks out teeth with an entrechat
then pirouettes on his toe.
With a flick of the hip
and a backward flip
he blackens eyes. It's no surprise
he's the toast of the south coast
no butts about it.
He handstands on noses
then poses, so bold,
and his somersaults to the groin
are a joy to behold.

Alf
is an aggrobat.

Alfreda

His sister Alfreda
was somewhat gentler
(though some would argue
even mentler).

A juggler who would only juggle
with objects beginning with A
like acorns, armchairs and armadillos
alarm clocks and albatrosses
aspidistras, and one day
an alligator
which went straight for the juggler.

Cousin Fosbury

Cousin Fosbury
took his highjumping seriously.
To ensure a floppier flop
he consulted a contortionist
and had his vertebrae removed
by a backstreet vertebraeortionist.

Now he clears 8 foot with ease
and sleeps with his head
tucked under his knees.

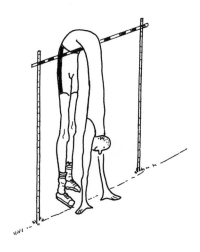

Cousin Ivor

Cousin Ivor, an ace
grand prix driver
won only one race
and the prix was a fiver.

Two laps of the track
at Wagga Waggaroo
against a blind
ex-boxing kangaroo.

(Although Ivor won by a short leg
there are those who vouch
that the roo had a beer keg
sewn into its pouch).

Unabashed, he downed a jeroboam
of sauvignon white
then crashed on the way home
serving him right.

Aunt Agatha

Aunt Agatha
blooded at five
loves to hunt foxes
and eat them alive.
No horsewoman,
she prefers to run
with the hounds.

On all fours
shod in running-
gloves and shoes,
no dog can match her
and once on the scent
nose smell-bent
no horse can catch her.

And she snaps
and she barks
and she urges the pack
onward on
to her bushy-tailed snack.

Tongue flapping
huntingpink suit
nostrils aflare
beware any hare
caught napping
en route.

And she snaps
and she barks
and she urges the pack
onward on
to her bushy-tailed snack.

D'ye ken Aunt Agatha
in her coat so gay
D'ye ken Aunt Agatha
at the close of day
houndsurrounded
tearing into foxflesh.

Uncle 'enery

Uncle 'enery
whose career in the ring
spanned almost two rounds
was a boxer of many parts.
He had: nerves of steel
        a will of iron
        a heart of gold
        a jaw of glass

alas.

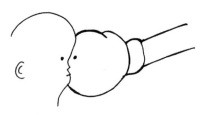

Old Mac

Old Mac, seventyodd
and eyes akimbo
was a prizefighter
in his youth.

Some nights in the bar
when he's had a few
he'll spar
with ghosts of pugilists
long since counted out.

Old Mac, still in training
for his final bout.

Eno

To be a sumo wrestler
    It pays to be fat.
'Nonsense,' said Eno,
    'I don't believe that.'

So he took his skinny
    little frame
to Tokyo
    in search of fame.

But even with God on
    his side
Eno got trod on
    and died.

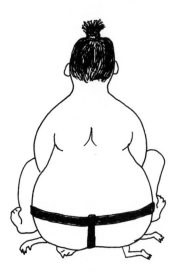

48

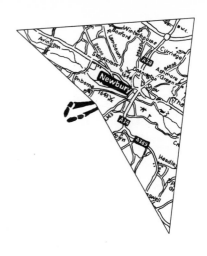

Marvin

Never hangglide
with a hangover
as Marvin did
near Andover.

Dying for a whisky
to straighten his head
'Just one for the road'
is in fact what he said
Saw the pub on the left
turned right instead

Hit the M23 near the junction of the A303.

(Now, if he had turned left at the A34 he would have
carried on to Newbury and swung a right at the A339
to Basingstoke. Alternatively, had he taken the A3057,
he might have avoided the road works and then had
the choice of reaching the M27 just south of Romsey,
or coming off at the A30 and going straight through to
Salisbury. Anyway, it's too late now, he's dead.)

Uncle Terry

Uncle Terry was a skydiver.
He liked best
the earth spread out beneath him
like a springcleaned counterpane.
The wind his safety net.

He free fell every day
and liked it so much
he decided to stay.
And they say he's still there
sunbathing in the air.

He sleeps each night
tucked up in moonlight
wakes at dawn
and chases clouds.

Living   off   the   food   birds   bring

Uncle   Terry   on   the   wing

away   from   it   all

dizzy   with   joy.

Barry Bungee

Barry Bungee
who loved to dive
thrust himself upon fate
and didn't survive.

Life and death
it was just a game
To Bungee-jumping
gave his name.

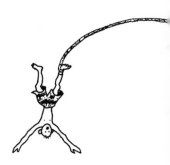

The first and only
jump he made
was from City Hall
in Adelaide.

Securing the bungee
to the base
he scaled the building
at a leisurely pace.

And from the roof
hands on hips
surveyed a crowd
biting its lips

then jumped. The bungee
coiled like a garden hose.
Only the ground
kept its mouth closed.

53

Uncle Jason

Uncle Jason, an ace in the Royal Flying Corps
grew up and old into a terrrible borps.
He'd take off from tables to play the Great Worps
stretch out his arms and crash to the florps.

His sister, an exSister (now rich) of the Porps,
would rorps forps morps: 'Encorps! Encorps!'

Cousin Christ

Cousin Christ (né Derek)
got out of bed at 8 to meditate.
Lacking a desert, he wandered
on Blackheath for 40 days
and 40 nights before being
arrested by two pharisees
in a panda car. 'Father,
forgive them,' he said.
And father, a door-to-door
used toupée salesman from Lewisham
did.

TOUPEE!

Cousin Fiona

Cousin Fiona
from near the top drawer
is a blueblood donor
and Kensington bore.

A moderate showjumper
plain and weakwilled
Cousin Fiona
is never funfilled.

For what she wants
but will never admit
is a man to take her by the bit.

Someone to
jog with
snog with
look in her eyes
canter
banter
romanticize

Someone to
lead her
to pastures new
someone to
share her
pony-made-for-two.

And Fiona sleeps in a saddlesoaped room
and dreams of a pinstripe-jodhpured groom
and crop in hand, she gallops into moonlit gymkhanas
to ride gentleshod over her sinning nude
sinewed broncoing buck
giddyup   giddyup   giddy   up   up   up.

And Fiona weeps after her lonely ride
always the bridle, never the bride.

Maybelline

Let's

hear

it

for

Maybelline

the

un-

sung

queen

of

the

TRAMPOLINE

sung

queen

of

the

TRAMPOLINE

Big Arth

Big Arth from Penarth
was a forward and a half.
Though built like a peninsula
with muscles like pink slagheaps
and a face like a cheese grater
he was as graceful and fast
as a greased cheetah.

A giraffe in the lineout
a rhino in the pack
he never passed forward
when he should've passed back
and once in possession
s ˡ ᵃ ᵃ ˡ o ᵐ e ᵈ his way
through the opposition.

And delicate?
Once for a lark
at Cardiff Arms Park
Big Arth
converted a softboiled egg
from the halfway line.

No doubt about it,
he was one of the best players in the second team.

Accrington Stan

A more talented footballer
   Never ran on a pitch
Than Accrington Stan
   Who might have been rich.

He could pass a ball
   He could score a goal
(But he couldn't pass a betting-shop
   So now he's on the dole).

The Hon. Nicholas Frayn

The Hon. Nicholas Frayn
who threw the javelin
would always travelin
a chauffeur-driven plane.
He somewhat lacked a chin
but always threw to win
and was notoriously vain.

He used only monogrammed javelins
sapphire-tipped and silver-plated
and was rated good enough to win his blue.
One day at a meeting in Crewe
he tripped and ran himself through
and though bleeding profusely
from a wound in his side
carried on gamely to finish next to last.
Then died.

Aunty Ann

Aunty Ann
an anti-angler
would dangle a
dead herring
on the end of a line.

A warning sign
to fishes
that man could be
vicious.

Not a popular figure
among the coarse
fishing crowd
she was found floating
one morning
in the river near Stroud.

At the memorial service
in an underwater church
the mourners were grayling
chub and perch,
salmon, pike and trout
who prayed, wet-eyed
then drifted out
to witness above
a heavenly banquet.

De profundis one by one
Temptation proved too great
Like angels falling into the sun
they rose, and took the bait.

Uncle Leo

Uncle Leo's sole ambition
was to be a liontamer
so he enrolled for classes at nightschool
and practised at home on his wife.

Aunt Elsa at first had reservations
but having once acquired
a taste for raw meat and the lash
she came on by leaps and bounds.

And after only 6 months
Uncle Leo announced with some pride
that his wife had opened her mouth
and he'd put his head inside.

One afternoon, however
while he was changing the sawdust
in the bathroom, Aunt Elsa escaped
mauled 2 boy scouts and a traffic warden
before being captured by the RSPCA.

Now a tamed Uncle Leo, give him his due
visits her daily at Regent's Park Zoo.

Uncle Len

Uncle Len
a redundant gamekeeper
strangled cuckoos.
He didn't give a f — whose
            c — oos
he strangled
as long as he silenced
as many as he could.

Last March in Bluebell Wood
while reaching for the season's
first feathered victim
he fell forty feet
broke his neck
and screaming,
unwittingly heralded spring.

Elmer Hoover

Elmer Hoover
on vac from
Vancouver
went fishing
off the Pier Head.

He caught 2 dead rats
dysentery
and a shoal of slimywhite balloonthings
which he brought home in a jamjar.
'Mersey cod,' we told him.

So he took the biggest
back to Canada.
Had it stuffed, mounted,
and displayed over the fireplace
in his trophy room.

'But you shudda seen
the one that got away,'
he would say.
Nonplussing his buddies.

Uncle Jed

Uncle Jed
Durham bred
raced pigeons
for money.

He died
a poor man
however

as the pigeons
were invariably
too quick for him.

Cousin Daisy

Cousin Daisy's
favourite sport
was standing
on streetcorners.

She contracted
with ease
a funny disease.
Notwithstanding.

Cousin Nell

Cousin Nell
married a frogman
in the hope
that one day
he would turn into
a handsome prince.

Instead he turned into
a sewage pipe
near Gravesend
and was never seen again.

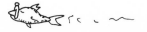